CELTIC MYTHS & LEGENDS

AS TOLD BY PHILIP ARDAGH

ILLUSTRATED BY G BARTON CHAPPLE

MYTH OR LEGEND?	2
HEROES OF CELTIC MYTHS AND LEGENDS	4
LLEW LLAW GYFFES ~ THE BRIGHT ONE	7
LUG ~ THE MASTER OF MASTERS	13
DEIRDRE ~ A LIFE OF SORROW	19
ARTHUR AND THE SWORD IN THE STONE	25
THE DEATH OF KING ARTHUR	31
CUCHULAIN ~ THE HOUND OF CULAN	37
THE CHANGELING OF GREEN KNOLL	43
INDEX	48

 Belitha Press

MYTH OR LEGEND?

Long before people could read or write, stories were passed on by word of mouth. Every time they were told, they changed a little, with a new character added here and a twist to the plot there. From these ever-changing tales, myths and legends were born.

WHAT IS A MYTH?

A myth is a traditional story that isn't based on something that really happened and is usually about superhuman beings. Myths are made up, but often help to explain local customs or natural phenomena.

WHAT IS A LEGEND?

A legend is very like a myth. The difference is that a legend might be based on an event that really happened, or a person who really existed. That's not to say that the story hasn't changed over the years. King Arthur probably did exist, but can't have done all the amazing things the Celts say he did.

WHO WERE THE CELTS?

The Celts originally occupied much of the British Isles and beyond. But after the Roman invasion of Britain in the first century AD, the Celts were limited to Ireland, Wales, Cornwall, the Western Isles of Scotland and Brittany – an area in northern France that was once part of the ancient country of Gaul. The Celts were called the Galli by the Romans, which is where the word 'Gaelic' comes from, as in the Gaelic language spoken by many Celts. Although the origins of a particular myth or legend may come from one particular region, versions were told by Celts everywhere.

This map of the British Isles and the northern coastline of continental Europe shows the main areas where Celts lived after the Roman invasion of Britain in the first century AD. The myths and legends in this book come from these Celtic regions.

WESTERN ISLES
OF SCOTLAND

IRELAND

WALES

CORNWALL

BRITTANY

One of the finest examples of Celtic metalwork is the Ardagh Chalice. This large silver cup is famous for its fine engraving and discs of red enamel. It is over 1000 years old.

How do we Know?

Many medieval records of Celtic myths survive to this day. For example, a written record of King Arthur's death dates back to about 955 AD. Celtic myths became popular again in the 19th and early 20th centuries. This was when the Romantic movement in art, music and literature brought new life to these tales of brave knights and beautiful ladies.

Note from the Author

Myths and legends from different cultures were told in different ways. The purpose of this book is to tell new versions of these old Celtic stories, not to try to copy the way in which they were first told. I hope that you enjoy them and that this book will make you want to find out more about the Celts and their myths and legends.

HEROES OF CELTIC MYTHS & LEGENDS

In this book, you can find out about some of the
best-known Celtic heroes and the fantastic myths
and legends that have grown up around them.
Here is a list of just some of the characters you
will meet along the way. Alternative spellings
of their names are shown in brackets.

ARIANROD Mother of Llew. She was
tricked by Gwydion into having his child.

ARTHUR King of the Britons. Arthur
probably existed, but much earlier than
the age of the knights in shining armour.
Married to Guinevere.

BALOR Fomorian chieftain with
an evil eye, who faced Lug in battle.

BLODEUWEDD Wife of Llew, made by
Math from flowers woven together by magic.

CHANGELING A faery child swapped
with a human baby at birth. Usually lazy
and clumsy.

CONCHOBAR (Conor) Pronounced
Kon-ko-bar. King of Ulster, hero and
villain of many Irish myths.

CUCHULAIN (Cuchullain, Cuchulan)
Pronounced *Koo-Kul-in*. Ireland's greatest
warrior of all time. Son of Lug and
Dechtire.

CULAN Blacksmith and owner of the
hound killed by Setanta.

DECHTIRE Sister of King Conchobar
and mother of Cuchulain.

DEIRDRE Daughter of Fedlimid.
It was prophesied that she would lead
to Ireland's ruin.

EMER Daughter of Forgal the Wily,
wife of Cuchulain.

FAERIES Another name for the Little
People. They are especially common in
Ireland where they are called leprechauns.

FOMORS Hideous giants who invaded Ireland and faced the forces of Lug.

GUINEVERE King Arthur's queen. Loved by Sir Lancelot.

GWYDION Father of Llew and nephew of the ruler and sorcerer, Math.

LANCELOT Arthur's friend and greatest knight, secretly in love with Guinevere.

LITTLE PEOPLE Faeries, common in Celtic folklore. They are often fine sword makers and blacksmiths.

LLEW LLAW GYFFES (Lleu Law Gyffes) Welsh hero of many adventures. His mother Arianrod was tricked by Gwydion into having this child.

LUG (Lugh) Immortal High King of Ireland, Master of All Arts.

MATH Magician ruler of the Welsh realm of Gwynedd.

NAOISE Brother of Ardan and Ainle, the sons of Usnech, nephew to Conchobar and lover of Deirdre.

NUADA King of the Tuatha Dé Dannan, the rulers of all Ireland. He had a silver hand.

SETANTA Cuchulain's name before he killed the hound of Culan.

TUATHA DE DANANN The People of the goddess Danu, later seen as gods of Ireland themselves.

Shared Heroes

The best myths have often been absorbed into the myths of more than one hero, and experts believe that some heroes are the same person given a different name and background. For example, it has been suggested that the Welsh character Llew and the Irish character Lug are one and the same person – and that the town of Lyon in Brittany is named after him.

Appealing to an Audience

It is easy to see how this chopping and changing of stories came about. These stories were originally spoken, not written down. Every time a Celt told a myth or legend, he or she would add local landmarks or events to make the story come alive to the people who were listening. Events in Brittany, for example, were changed when they were told in Scotland, Ireland or Wales.

LLEW LLAW GYFFES THE BRIGHT ONE

In one of the most famous Welsh myths, Gwydion used magic to trick Arianrod into having his child. She never even knew their son existed until his fourth birthday, when Gwydion took him to meet her at her castlc, Caer Arianrod, overlooking the sea.

'This is our son,' said Gwydion, proudly pushing the boy forward into the light.

'It was a terrible thing you did,' said Arianrod, 'using magic to trick me like that.' She looked at the boy. He was tall and strong for his age and had bright, burning eyes like his father's.

'What is his name?' she asked.

'He has no name,' said Gwydion. 'I thought it only right that you should be the one to choose it.'

'So no one else shall name him?' asked Arianrod, still hurt by Gwydion's trickery.

'No one but you,' Gwydion assured her. He hoped that meeting her child like this might melt Arianrod's heart and make her forgive him the wrongs he had done her in the past.

'Then the boy shall remain nameless forever!' cried Arianrod. 'Now go... and take the proof of your trickery with you.'

Gwydion took their son's hand, turned and strode towards the castle gates. Suddenly he stopped in his stride and looked back at Arianrod.

'I'll see you name the boy!' he swore. 'Our son shall have a name!'

Down on the seashore, Gwydion used his magic to trick Arianrod a second time. He wove a powerful spell, and magic hung heavy in the air like the sea mist all around them. When the mist lifted, both he and his son had taken on a different appearance, a moored boat had appeared on the water, and a shoemaker's tools and materials had been set up on the beach.

Soon news reached Arianrod that a cobbler and his apprentice had sailed into the cove. She sent one of her servants instructions to have them make her a pair of their finest shoes.

This was just as Gwydion had hoped. He made the most beautiful pair of shoes you can imagine… but deliberately made them just too big. The following day, the servant returned and asked the cobbler to make her mistress another pair of shoes, the same as the first, only slightly smaller. This Gwydion did, but this time he deliberately made them too small. The next morning, Arianrod came down to the cove herself to ask them to cut the leather to fit her soles.

There she witnessed the golden-haired apprentice fire an arrow into the air and strike a wren, the tiniest of birds and one of the hardest targets to hit.

Arianrod was impressed. 'The bright one has a steady hand!' she smiled. 'What is his name?'

'He had no name until this moment,' said Gwydion, 'but now you have given him one. He is the Bright One – the lion – with a Steady Hand,' which, in the old language, was Llew Llaw Gyffes.

As he spoke, the boat disappeared from the water, the tools and materials disappeared from the beach and Gwydion and his son were themselves once more.

Furious that she had been tricked once again, Arianrod flew into a rage, and Gwydion tried in vain to make her proud of their son.

'Llew is a fine name for a warrior, don't you agree?' he asked. 'See how quickly he's already grown.'

'But what warrior can fight without armour or weapons?' said Arianrod. 'I swear that Llew shall have neither unless I give them to him, and that is something I shall never do.'

With that, she started to climb up the winding path back to Caer Arianrod.

Llew grew into a hearty young man in half the time it would take any ordinary soul. He was handsome, strong and a skilled horse rider, and it was soon time for him to learn how to use a sword.

So Gwydion and Llew found themselves once more at the huge gates of Caer Arianrod. And once again Gwydion used his magic to cast a spell to change their appearance.

This time they became a bard and his servant. Bards were proud wandering poets who entertained their audiences with epic poems about great feats of bravery. Gwydion and Llew were made very welcome by Arianrod and her court. They were well fed and given a grand chamber in which to spend the night.

While the rest of the castle was asleep, Gwydion climbed to the top of the highest tower of Caer Arianrod and stood facing the sea in the first glimmerings of morning light. A gentle breeze ruffled his hair as he muttered ancient words of illusion.

Arianrod awoke to the cries of her sentries, warning her that an enemy fleet had entered the bay and was about to lay siege to the castle. A soldier burst into Gwydion's chamber carrying a handful of weapons. He asked Gwydion and Llew to take up arms and help protect the castle, but Gwydion refused.

'This is not our fight,' he said. 'We are bards, not warriors. Leave us be.'

When news of this reached Arianrod, she knocked at their chamber door and entered.

'Your poems talked of brave deeds and heroic acts,' she said. 'Are they just words to you? Will you not live up to them and fight my enemy alongside me?'

'Very well,' said Gwydion. 'But give the boy some armour.'

Soon a pair of Arianrod's maidens returned with armour which Arianrod buckled to the youth.

'Now give the boy weapons,' said Gwydion, 'and we shall prepare.'

As soon as Arianrod heaped a pile of weapons into Llew's arms, every ship in the bay drifted away like the illusions that they really were, and Gwydion and Llew were revealed as their true selves.

Arianrod was stunned. 'Is there no end to your trickery?' she asked, aghast. 'Well, here's a curse that you cannot trick me into undoing!'

She strode across the stone floor to the chamber window and threw the wooden shutters wide open.

'I swear by all things sacred that there is, never was and never shall be a woman from any of the races in all the world who will take Llew as her husband,' she screamed, the wind carrying her words across the sea.

Arianrod thought she had been clever with her curse. Her careful wording had made sure that Gwydion could not raise the dead to give his son a bride, nor wait until a girl grew into a woman after the curse had been made.

'Is, was and never shall,' were the words she had chosen, and she felt sure they were the right ones. She was satisfied that no woman could ever take Llew as her husband.

But Arianrod was mistaken. By being thorough and excluding all women from any of the races in all the world, she had left Gwydion with hope.

'What about a bride not born of *any* of the races... not born of people?' he said. 'This might be the way to break the curse!'

'You want me to marry a she-wolf?' asked his puzzled son.

'No,' laughed Gwydion. 'We will use magic to make you a wife!'

So Gwydion took Llew to his uncle, the great magician Math, who ruled the realm of Gwynedd from his mighty throne. Gwydion told him of the curse and his ideas for breaking it.

'I will give you a bride, Llew,' he said and ordered Gwydion and Llew to pick the blossoms of oak trees, the flowers of broom bushes and the petals of the meadowsweet, and to bring them to him.

When this was done, he wove them together with strong bonds of magic to create the most beautiful and graceful woman Llew had ever seen.

'I have never seen such beauty,' he said in wonder. 'She has the beauty of all Nature.'

'She is to be called Blodeuwedd or Flower Face,' said Math. 'She will take you as her husband.'

So now Llew was strong and handsome, had a proud name, was a great warrior with armour and weapons and – after a magnificent wedding feast – was married to the beautiful Blodeuwedd.

Llew took Blodeuwedd to live in Mur Castell in the hills of Ardudwy – lands given to him by Math as a wedding gift – where he became a wise and much-loved ruler of his people.

But Llew's life was not all happiness. Later, Blodeuwedd betrayed and killed him but, once again, Math came to his rescue. He used his magic to bring one of the Celts' greatest heroes back to life.

LUG - THE MASTER OF MASTERS

Tara was the high seat of the Irish Kings. Here, King Nuada gathered the best of his people to form a council of war against the Fomors – the hideous giants from across the sea.

After all the others had gathered, a stranger arrived at the entrance to Tara. Though young and unscarred, he was dressed as a warrior king. He knocked on the gate.

'Who are you?' asked the gatekeeper. 'What do you want?'

'I am Lug,' replied Lug, 'and I wish to join the council.'

'Many seek entry, but very few are admitted,' said the gatekeeper. 'Only those who are the true masters of their craft may enter here.'

'I'm a blacksmith,' said Lug.

'Tara has a blacksmith,' said the gatekeeper.

'I'm a carpenter,' said Lug.

'Tara has a carpenter,' replied the gatekeeper.

'I'm a poet and a storyteller,' continued Lug.

'We already have the best within these walls,' snapped the gatekeeper.

Lug tried healer, magician, musician... and each time the gatekeeper told him that the master of such a craft was already inside Tara.

'You may already have a master for each of these crafts, but I am master of them all,' said Lug. 'Surely that gives me the right to enter?'

The gatekeeper heard a ring of truth in the newcomer's words. There was no boastfulness in the stranger's voice. Either he really was as masterful as he claimed or, at least, he believed that he was.

'I shall speak with King Nuada and ask whether he grants you entry,' said the gatekeeper.

When he entered the great hall and told the king about Lug and his claims at the gates of Tara, all those around him laughed.

'You bother the king with such obvious lies?' one grinned. 'Send this imposter on his way.'

But Nuada banged his fist on the arm of his throne, demanding silence. There was a time when the king had no fist to bang. His hand had been cut off in the battle that made his people, the Tuatha Dé Danann, rulers of Ireland. Nuada had a hand made from silver, but now it was as good as new, thanks to the healing powers of one called Miach. Some had doubted the powers of Miach in the beginning, just as Lug was being doubted now.

'One as masterful as this Lug claims to be should have no trouble playing fidchell,' commented the king. 'Set up a board and pieces and let's see how well he does against our best players.'

So the board game, a bit like chess, was set up outside Tara, and Lug took up the challenge. He not only beat every man and woman he played, he beat them as they'd never been beaten before. He played with such amazing speed it was difficult to imagine when he found time to think. He even invented a move never used before.

On hearing the news of Lug's victory, the king came to meet him at the gates in person, led him inside and sat him in the one unfilled seat on the council – that of the person with the greatest knowledge.

Not everyone was happy with the way King Nuada welcomed this young newcomer. Who did Lug think he was? Ogma, the champion of Tara, decided to put him in his place. He stepped in front of Lug's seat, bent down and – with eyes bulging and muscles as hard as iron – pulled an enormous flagstone from the floor.

Some say that it had taken over eighty oxen to drag the stone into place, and now Ogma was rolling it across the courtyard and out of the gates of Tara.

'I wonder if the newcomer would put it back in place for me?' grinned Ogma, sweat pouring from his red face.

Lug said nothing. He knew that he was being tested – when all he wanted was to be accepted. He strode through the gates and a moment later, to the complete and utter amazement of all those inside Tara, the huge flagstone was tossed over the wall and came crashing down in its original place, landing perfectly square in the hole it had left behind.

After that, Lug played them all such sweet music and sang such beautiful songs that the people of Tara had never felt so refreshed and ready to make plans for war. They gave Lug the title Samildanach, which means Master of All Arts.

Then King Nuada made an important decision. He decided that, because Lug was so gifted, he should lead the council of war. He also decided that because this was the job of a king, he should hand over the crown to Lug whilst the plans were laid.

This is how it came to be that Lug sat on the throne at Tara – with Nuada on his right in the seat of knowledge – when important strategies were made.

The planning continued. Days became weeks, and soon a year had passed, and still the hideous Fomorian giants had not come. Lug went back to the people of Mananánn mac Lir. When the Fomors finally landed on Irish soil, Lug took his people with him to face them.

With so much careful planning and such strong magic, it seemed that the Tuatha Dé Danann would be victorious. Tara's magicians turned the trees and rocks of Ireland into warriors to fight the Fomors. Tara's cup bearers – those who served wine in the royal household – wove a spell that made the twelve rivers and twelve lakes of Ireland invisible to the enemy. This meant that no matter how thirsty the Fomors were, they could find no water in the land.

Magic spears were also used which never missed their target.

Diancecht – whose son, Miach, had healed Nuada's severed hand – used his knowledge to heal all the warriors' wounds, except for those who had lost their heads. Each night, the dead warriors were taken to a special spring by Diancecht and his handmaidens. Here the fallen were bathed, their injuries washed away, and they were brought back to life.

News of the secret of this magic spring finally reached a chief of the Fomorian army. Named Balor, he was one of its fiercest warriors and, by a quirk of fate, he was also Lug's own grandfather. Balor ordered his men to heap stones upon the source, where the water sprang from the earth. Soon they had built a huge cairn and the healing waters were trapped deep underground. Now Balor felt ready for his army to meet his enemies face-to-face in battle.

As the Fomorian army gathered on the eastern side of the plain of Moytura, and the Tuatha Dé Danann gathered on the west side, there was unrest in the Danann ranks. News spread that the magic spring was gone, and their spirits fell. The Fomors were giants, and they were many. What chance did the Tuatha Dé Danann have against them?

Hearing that the troops were disheartened, Lug rode up and down the lines of soldiers offering words of encouragement. Catching sight of his glinting armour, one of the soldiers commented, 'Strange how today the sun chooses to rise in the west instead of the east!'

Then the battle commenced. The Tuatha Dé Danann fought bravely, none more so than Queen Macha – wife of King Nuada – who fought at her husband's side. Nuada was killed by Balor, and Macha also perished. Soon the battlefield was piled high with bodies and running with blood. Many Irish chiefs died that day, but still the battle raged.

The hideous giant Balor had an evil eye. The eyelid was closed and kept in place by a special ring of brass. The ring was so heavy that it could only be lifted by four men. This was because one glance from Balor's eye would kill whoever it fell upon. This made it a mighty weapon against enemies, but also a danger to friends.

Balor faced Lug now – grandfather against grandson. The Fomorian chief ordered his henchmen to his side.

'Lift the brass ring to free my eyelid so that I might gaze upon this little champion of the Tuatha Dé Danann,' he roared.

Four of the Fomors stepped forward and began to lift the ring. But Lug was ready for them. He pulled out his sling shot and let loose a stone that hit the half-opened eye. The stone was a magic one and it struck the giant's evil eye with such force that the eyeball was fired through the back of Balor's skull and on to the battlefield. When it stopped spinning in the mud, the evil eye came to rest its gaze upon a huge group of Fomorian warriors, who instantly dropped down dead.

Seizing the moment, Lug raised his sword and led his army through the break in the Fomors' line. Victory was theirs, and those Fomors who were not slain fled from Irish soil, never to return.

Lug ruled as an Irish High King for forty years, though what became of him after that is shrouded in mystery. Some say he drowned. Others say that he is a god and will live forever.

DEIRDRE - A LIFE OF SORROW

This Irish myth tells the tragic tale of a woman called Deirdre and a prophecy that would lead to the downfall of all Ireland. This ancient story, which has been told and retold in many forms, also has strong links with the Celts of Scotland.

Conchobar, King of Ulster, was at a feast given by Fedlimid. With him were the Red Branch, his greatest warriors. During the festivities, news reached the high table that Fedlimid's wife had given birth to their long-awaited child – a baby girl. There was much rejoicing. Then suddenly Cathbad the Druid rose from his seat and tried to speak above the noise.

'This is no cause for celebration,' he bellowed and, because all those present knew that he had the gift of prophecy, they fell silent to hear his words.

'This is a terrible day for Ireland and for the Red Branch, for this tiny babe shall grow into a woman who shall lead to Ireland's ruin and the destruction of the Red Branch! She must be called Deirdre, which means troubler,' he declared.

One of the Red Branch leapt to his feet and pulled his sword from its scabbard. 'I say we slay the babe Deirdre now before she can do any harm!' he cried, and there were rumblings of agreement from his fellow warriors.

'Hold fast!' commanded the king. 'We are guests of Fedlimid. We are here at his invitation. Would you have us slaughter the newly-born daughter of our host?'

The warrior looked shame-faced and returned to his seat.

'I say we send Deirdre away to a place where she knows nothing of what has been prophesied here today and then, when she is fully grown, I will take her as my wife. As queen, she will love all Ireland. As my wife, the Red Branch shall be her protectors. Why, then, would she wish them ill?' said Conchobar.

The assembled company cheered. This was an admirable solution from a wise king. Relieved that the king had spared his new-born daughter's life, but horrified by the druid's prophecy, Fedlimid gave Deirdre to Conchobar who took her in his arms.

Now, the king sent the baby to be brought up in a small castle in the forest, where she was cared for by a nurse, a forester and a woman called Levarcham. But only Levarcham knew who this child really was.

Deirdre had a happy childhood and grew into a caring and loving young woman, but the only man she ever saw was the forester.

One cold winter's day, she sat staring out of the window on to the snow-covered ground.

'I wish I had a husband whose skin was as white as snow,' she sighed.

Then, a trickle of blood from a slaughtered calf came from under the door of a shed in the courtyard and stained the snow bright crimson.

'I wish I had a husband whose cheeks were as red as blood,' she added.

A hungry raven swooped down at the sight of the blood and flew off in search of food.

'I wish I had a husband whose hair was as black as the raven's feathers,' she finished.

Levarcham was distressed to see the girl she'd grown to think of as her own daughter looking so sad.

'I know a man who has snow-white skin, blood-red cheeks and hair that's raven-black,' she said. 'His name is Naoise. He is one of the three Sons of Usnech, and is the king's nephew.'

Deirdre pleaded with Levarcham to meet this man. Against her better judgement, Levarcham gave in and invited Naoise to the castle in the forest. The two met and fell in love.

In time, Naoise discovered that this fair maiden was Deirdre of the prophecy whom his uncle, King Conchobar, had pledged to marry.

'I can come and visit you here in the castle in the forest,' he said, 'but we can never be together.'

'Why not?' said Deirdre. 'Don't tell me that you don't have the same feelings for me as I for you. I know you do.'

'Of course I do,' cried Naoise, 'but Conchobar has pledged to marry you and he is our king.'

'Then we shall go to a place, far from here, where he does not rule,' protested Deirdre.

And so it came to be that Deirdre avoided the ever-watchful eye of Levarcham and fled with Naoise to Scotland, accompanied by Naoise's brothers, Ardan and Ainle, who travelled with them for protection.

Years passed and Deirdre and Naoise were blissfully happy in Scotland in a place called Alba. But Conchobar still wanted to take Deirdre as his wife. He claimed that it was to protect all Ireland and the Red Branch against Cathbad's prophecy of ruin and destruction. But the truth was that Conchobar had heard reports of Deirdre's beauty and wanted her for himself. He had learnt of her whereabouts and decided to send someone to bring the runaways home.

The king chose Fergus for the task because he was one of the most famed heroes of all Ireland. 'Go in my name and bring Deirdre and my nephew Naoise back to Ulster,' he commanded.

'I will not force them, since they have done no harm,' said Fergus.

'I said nothing of force,' said the king. 'Offer them safe passage. Promise them that they are free to leave whenever they wish.'

Fergus travelled with his sons to show that his intentions were honourable and that he meant no harm. But Deirdre would not trust him. He told them of the king's promise, but still she feared a trap.

'We should go, beloved,' Naoise insisted. 'Conchobar is my uncle, and he has given his word as a king.'

Finally, Deirdre agreed to travel back to Ireland to hear what Conchobar had to say. Ardan and Ainle were eager to go too, for they missed the island of their birth.

As they were leaving, Deirdre began to sing a sorrowful song. This song later became known as *Farewell to Alba*, for Deirdre was never to return to Scotland.

Back on Irish soil, Conchobar tricked Fergus into parting company from the others. He invited him to an important feast and Fergus could not refuse him. Without their protector, meanwhile, Deirdre, Naoise and his brothers, and the sons of Fergus were all made welcome at the hall of the Red Branch, home to the King of Ulster's finest warriors. They didn't suspect a trap until Levarcham – who, remember, had brought up Deirdre from a baby – came to warn them.

'Prepare to defend yourselves or flee this place!' she cried, but it was too late. Moments later, the doors flew open and Conchobar's men were upon them.

There are many stories about how well Deirdre's party fought against the Red Branch. The three Sons of Usnech stood around her, protecting her with shield and spear, and each one killed over three hundred of their enemies. But they were hopelessly outnumbered and the king had another weapon – the magic of Cathbad the Druid. Cathbad cast a spell upon them and they were defeated.

The Sons of Usnech – Deirdre's beloved Naoise and his brothers Ardan and Ainle – were taken away and beheaded. Before the blade touched Naoise's neck, he raised his eyes to the heavens and swore his everlasting love for Deirdre.

When, later, Deirdre stumbled upon his open grave, she let down her hair and sang the saddest song ever sung on Irish soil. Throwing herself on to Naoise's body, Deirdre then gave him three kisses and died.

Hearing the news, King Conchobar was not displeased. He ordered that Deirdre be buried next to Naoise and that a wooden stake be hammered into each grave. 'That way we can be sure that no magic can bring them back to life,' he said.

Then he summoned Cathbad. 'See, Deirdre is dead, yet Ireland does not lie in ruins and the Red Branch is as strong as ever!' he crowed. 'Here's one prophecy of yours that won't be coming true, druid!'

But Conchobar had spoken too soon. It was no longer an honour to be a member of the Red Branch. Many came to see them as a group of fighters who carried out orders without a thought for Right or Truth and, finally, their numbers dwindled until they were no more.

Horrified by what the King of Ulster and his Red Branch had done, many of his subjects turned their backs on him and swore allegiance to another king. Now Irishman turned against Irishman. The prophecy had been fulfilled.

Meanwhile, the two wooden stakes driven into the graves of Deirdre and Naoise grew into a pair of yew trees. Their branches became entwined like the arms of lovers, embracing each other for eternity.

Arthur and the Sword in the Stone

Perhaps the best-known of all Celtic heroes is King Arthur, the legendary King of the Britons. The Welsh and Cornish claimed him as their own, and in Brittany he was seen as a god-like figure.

When the mighty King Uther Pendragon died, there was no prince in his castle to take his place and to rule the Britons. It was not long before quarrels broke out about who should be the new king.

The head bishop ordered that all Lords should come to the great church in the capital to attend Christmas mass. When mass was done, the bishop led them into the churchyard where, to everyone's amazement, there was an extraordinary sight to behold. There stood a huge stone. On that stone was an anvil and, sticking through the anvil into the stone, was a sword.

'Whoever pulls this sword from this stone and anvil is the rightful King of the Britons,' said the bishop, though he did not say how the sword came to be there.

Every Lord in attendance took his turn to try to pull the sword, but it moved for no one.

Every New Year's Eve there was a special jousting tournament in the capital, and knights and their squires came from all over the land to prove their skills. One such knight, a true and loyal follower of the late King Pendragon, was Sir Ector, who lived deep in the countryside. But news of the sword in the stone had not yet reached him.

This New Year's Eve, the tournament was to be a special one for Sir Ector and his family. It was to be the first at which his son, Sir Kay, would fight as a knight. The third member of the party to attend the tournament was Arthur, whom Sir Ector had brought up as if he were his own flesh and blood. Arthur would act as Kay's squire, attending him, tending his horse, and looking after his armour and weapons.

On the morning they set off for the tournament, Sir Ector's wife and all the staff were lined up outside their castle to wish them Godspeed and a safe journey.

Kay's mother kissed him on both cheeks.

'Though winning is important, a knight's honour is more important still,' she reminded him. 'Fight fairly and be true.'

'I will, mother,' Sir Kay beamed, climbing astride his horse.

'Be good, Arthur,' she said, kissing him in turn, for she truly loved him as if he were her own son, which he assumed he was. 'You'll make a fine squire for your brother, and it won't be long until you too are a knight.'

Bursting with boyish pride, Arthur climbed upon his horse – less grand than Sir Kay's steed, admittedly, but one he loved dearly.

Then it was time to depart.

'This year we shall win great honours!' said Sir Ector. 'I feel sure of it.'

He gave his mount a tap with his spurs, and the three horses began the three-day ride to the New Year's Eve tournament.

On the first night of the journey, Sir Ector's party slept at the house of a friend who hadn't yet heard news of the sword in the stone. The talk that evening at the dinner table was of jousts, not of the extraordinary sword that would reveal the true King of the Britons.

The second night – just half a day's ride from the tournament – there was talk of little else at the tavern where Sir Ector, Sir Kay and Arthur were staying. But they were so tired from their travels that they went straight to their rooms and to bed, and heard nothing of it.

Meanwhile in the tavern below, men from far and wide gossiped about the sword and the future king.

'Whoever he is, he will be a fine champion,' said one, banging his drinking cup down on the oak table. 'It will take enormous strength to pull that sword from its place.'

The ale flowed, and the gossip continued through till morning.

So eager was Sir Kay to get to the tournament – for in previous years he had always been his father's squire, and not a knight in his own right – that the small party set off at first light.

It was as they reached the outskirts of the capital, and the tower of the great church was in sight, that Sir Kay realized that his scabbard was empty. He'd left his sword back at their lodgings.

'A fine knight at a tournament I'll make without a sword!' he laughed. 'I must return to the tavern to fetch it.'

'I'll go,' said Arthur. 'You mustn't miss the start of the joust. Besides, I am your squire and should have made sure your sword was with you.'

So Arthur hurried off back to the tavern, leaving Sir Ector and Sir Kay to enter the capital and to make their way to the jousting fields.

The sword, meanwhile, was nowhere to be found and Arthur was downhearted. What could he tell Kay? On his return, he passed the churchyard to the great church and saw the sword sticking from the anvil and the stone. 'What an extraordinary sight!' he thought.

Although ten knights were meant to guard it, none was at his post that day. Perhaps they were all at the joust. Perhaps magic was at work. Or perhaps it was fate that Kay had lost his sword in the first place, and now young Arthur was able to seize this sword unchallenged.

'A strange place to leave a sword,' he said to himself. 'I'll borrow it, for Kay must have a weapon.'

He strode across the churchyard and pulled the gleaming sword free from the stone with one clean stroke. It was as easy as pulling swords from a barrel of sand – something he sometimes did at home to treat old swords for rust.

'This is the finest sword I've ever seen,' he mused. 'An excellent substitute for Kay's missing weapon.' Then he hurried to the joust and handed it to the young man he thought of as his brother.

Since Sir Kay and his father had parted company with Arthur, they'd heard stories about the sword in the stone from others on the road long before they reached the tournament. They'd even found time to stop in the churchyard and marvel at it.

This meant that the moment Arthur handed it to him, Kay recognized the sword from the stone. An incredible feeling of excitement and power pulsed through his body as he clutched the sword of the rightful King of the Britons.

He hurried to Sir Ector.

'Father!' he cried. 'Father! I have the sword! I have the sword! I must be your rightful king!'

Sir Ector was amazed and took the mystical sword from his son's grasp. He studied the gold hilt and gleaming blade.

'This is indeed the sword from the churchyard,' he spluttered, in absolute amazement. 'How did you come by it, Kay? Did you pull it from the anvil and the stone?'

Somehow Kay felt less sure of himself now that the sword was no longer in his grasp. He felt like a knight at his first tournament... He felt like a son who had lied to his father... like a brother who had betrayed his own brother...

'No,' said Sir Kay, his head bowed. 'Arthur brought it to me.'

'Arthur?' gasped Sir Ector. 'We must go to him at once.'

Back in the churchyard, Sir Ector ordered Arthur to replace the sword in the anvil and the stone. Arthur did so and then Sir Ector and Sir Kay tried to pull it free. Try as they might, neither of them could pull the sword from the stone.

'Do as you did before, Arthur,' said Sir Ector.

Arthur obeyed, and the sword slid as easily from the anvil and the stone as it had the first time – only this time it was before the witnesses of an ever-growing crowd.

Again Arthur replaced the sword, and again he pulled it free. Sir Ector turned to the boy and looked him in the eye.

'Listen,' he said, 'for I have an important tale to tell.'

Then Sir Ector told Arthur of his true beginnings.

'I am not your real father,' he said. 'As a baby, you were brought to me by Merlin, magician and adviser to King Uther Pendragon, to be reared as my own. Now I realize that you must be the king's own flesh and blood. You are his son and heir.'

'You are not my true family?' asked Arthur with sadness.

'We are all your family,' said Sir Ector, with a hug, 'for you are Arthur, King of the Britons, and we are all your loyal subjects.'

A year later, Arthur was crowned king. He then set up court at Camelot and gathered together the Knights of the Round Table – the most famous knights in myth or legend.

THE DEATH OF KING ARTHUR

The sword from the stone was a fine weapon, but King Arthur was soon to own the finest sword of them all. This sword was so great and so powerful that it had a name – Excalibur. It was given to Arthur by the Lady of the Lake, and it would be returned to her when King Arthur was betrayed and killed.

Arthur built a castle at Camelot. Inside the castle was a huge round table where Arthur and his knights sat when they gathered to meet. The Knights of the Round Table were the greatest knights the world has ever seen. And the greatest of them all was Sir Lancelot from Brittany.

King Arthur and his knights had many adventures, and proved themselves honourable and chivalrous men. Their most glorious quest was for the Holy Grail – the cup from which Jesus Christ was said to have drunk at The Last Supper.

Arthur's queen was Guinevere, and they had married for love. This was against the advice of Merlin, the magician. Merlin – who had counselled King Uther Pendragon before him – had become Arthur's most trusted adviser.

'Beautiful though Guinevere is,' he warned, 'she will bring much grief and sorrow to this land. But, if you love her, nothing I can say will make you change your mind.'

For the magician knew that – deep in his heart – Sir Lancelot loved Guinevere too, and that no good would come of this.

It was more usual, however, for the king to take Merlin's advice. One such occasion was when the magician came to him with news of a dreadful prophecy.

'Sire,' he said. 'A man born on this May Day will be your undoing.'

'Then all boys of noble birth born on that day must be brought here to the castle, where they shall be brought up under my rules of chivalry,' said the king.

Arthur would not accept that prophecies could be broken, so all the male babies in the land were put aboard a ship to sail to Camelot.

A strange storm blew up out of nowhere. In the blinking of an eye, the calm waters were transformed into high, crashing waves and the ship was smashed against the rocks. The ship was wrecked and everyone on board perished – all, that is, except for a boy called Mordred who was washed up on the shore. Mordred was found by a kindly man who brought him up as his own.

When Mordred reached the age of fourteen, he was taken to the court at Camelot and presented to King Arthur who – knowing nothing of his history – made him welcome. From that day on, while presenting himself as an honourable man, Mordred worked towards the king's undoing.

He decided that the best way to defeat King Arthur and the Knights of the Round Table was not by attacking them with an outside force, but by turning knight against knight from within.

He knew that Sir Lancelot, the king's close friend, loved Guinevere, and began to spread lies about the two of them meeting secretly. Over time, he managed to convince twelve knights that they should kill Sir Lancelot for his disloyalty. Mordred planned to split the court of Camelot into two camps, as he knew that some knights would be against the king and some for him.

But when the twelve knights went to face Sir Lancelot, they were no match for him, and Lancelot survived.

Sadly, however, his friendship with Arthur did not. The king's mind had been poisoned by Mordred's rumours about Lancelot and Guinevere, and he became so jealous that he ordered that his own wife be burned at the stake for loving another man.

This went against everything King Arthur stood for, but the king was still the king and, carrying out his orders, Sir Gaheris and Sir Gareth tied their queen to the stake and lit the flames. As the flames at her feet began to dance and lick the edge of her flowing robe, Sir Lancelot galloped into the courtyard and rescued her.

Mordred's plan was working. The Knights of the Round Table split into two groups, with brother fighting brother. Leaving Guinevere in his castle, Lancelot fled to Brittany. King Arthur rounded up a force and went after him. With the king out of the country, Mordred claimed the crown for himself. Now all he wanted was Guinevere as his bride.

Mordred lied to Guinevere, telling her that Arthur had died in battle and that he, Mordred, was now rightful King of the Britons and that she must be his queen.

When news of this reached King Arthur, he hurried back to Britain and fought Mordred's forces. After much fighting, Mordred and Arthur agreed a parley – the two men would meet to discuss a peaceful settlement, while those on the battlefield would stop fighting and tend to their wounded and dying.

At the parley, Mordred admitted that he would never be able to claim the crown of all Britain while Arthur lived. He was no match for Arthur and the loyalty he brought out in his men. Arthur, on the other hand, knew that Mordred would always be a danger unless a lasting settlement could be reached, so he offered Mordred the dukedoms of Cornwall and Kent.

'And, when I die, the throne of the whole of Britain shall be yours,' he added.

Mordred was delighted with these terms. He couldn't have hoped for more.

No one would question Mordred's right to the crown now that he had been named King of the Britons by Arthur himself.

'Agreed!' he cried.

And that would have been the end of it, if a snake hadn't bitten the foot of one of Arthur's knights when the king returned to his camp on the battlefield. The knight – we know not who – raised his sword to strike the adder, but this was taken as a signal for the fighting to restart now that the parley was over... and the battle resumed more ferociously than ever before.

The battle was so bloody that when evening came there were only four people left standing out of many thousands. On one side was Mordred. On the other were King Arthur, Sir Lucan and Sir Bedivere.

'Lend me your spear,' the king ordered Sir Lucan. Arthur seized the spear and charged down the hill crying, 'Traitor, your death day has come!'

Though Arthur found his target and ran the spear through the traitor, Mordred still managed to deal the king a fatal wound.

As Arthur lay dying, he was able to pull his sword, Excalibur, from its scabbard and hand it to Sir Bedivere.

'Take this to the lake,' he instructed, 'and throw it in. Then come back and tell me what you saw.'

So Sir Bedivere took Excalibur, but could not bring himself to throw away the magical sword, so loved by the king. Instead, he hid it.

'It is done,' he said, returning to the dying Arthur.

'And what did you see?' asked the king.

'Nothing but ripples on the water,' said Sir Bedivere.

'Go and do as I asked,' said Arthur.

Bedivere returned to the lake, uncovered the sword, but once again could not bring himself to throw it into the water.

He returned to the battlefield for the second time, and, when asked by Arthur what he'd seen, he lied for the second time.

'I saw nothing but waves lapping the shore,' he said.

King Arthur looked deep into Sir Bedivere's eyes.

'That is not truly spoken. Why would you betray me after years of such loyalty?'

Shamed and saddened, Sir Bedivere went to the lake a third time. This time, he threw Excalibur as high and as far as he could.

It flew through the air in a graceful arc and, moments before it hit the water, an arm broke through the lake's surface to catch it. The arm brandished the sword three times and pulled it underwater.

When Bedivere told Arthur of this, the king smiled. Excalibur was with the Lady of the Lake once more. Then the dying king asked Bedivere to carry him to the water's edge where a funeral barge glided through the drifting mist. In it sat three silent women, draped in black. The dying king was lifted aboard the vessel and Sir Bedivere bade him farewell. The barge set sail for the Isle of Avalon where Arthur lies to this day.

Some say that King Arthur is not dead but is sleeping. They call him the 'once and future king'. They say that, in Britain's greatest hour of need, he will awake and bring his people even greater victories.

CUCHULAIN - THE HOUND OF CULAN

Cuchulain, Ireland's mightiest warrior, was
a handsome man. In battle, however, he took
on a horrifying form. His skeleton swivelled
inside his skin, one eye bulged and the other
shrank, sparks poured from his mouth,
and his body hissed with heat.

Conchobar, king of Ulster, had a beautiful sister called
Dechtire. At a feast to mark Dechtire's marriage to
Sualtam, a local chieftain, there was much celebration. When
Dechtire's wine goblet was refilled, she didn't notice a May
bug land in the liquid, and she swallowed it with a sip of wine.
A moment later she found herself in a deep, deep sleep and
Lug, the hero of a bygone age, appeared to her.

'I was in that May bug,' said Lug. 'It will grow inside you
and give you a son. Now come away with me and bring
your maidens to attend you.'

'But I cannot simply leave my own wedding feast,' protested
Dechtire. 'I am Sualtam's now, and he is mine.'

'No one will see you or your maidens,' Lug promised, and
he turned them into a flock of gleaming birds.

Nine months passed, and no one had seen sight nor sound of
Dechtire since she'd disappeared into thin air on her wedding
day... That is until a group of warriors out hunting one day
followed a flock of the most extraordinary birds they'd ever
seen. The flock led them to the place of the gods.

Night was falling and the hunters were greeted by a richly-dressed man who invited them to his palace, offering them food and shelter.

The hunters ate well and had nothing but praise for their mysterious host. But their sleep that night was interrupted by the cries of a new-born babe.

The following morning, their host greeted them once more, but this time they saw him for who he really was. It was Lug, and in his arms was a shining baby boy.

'This is my son,' he said, 'mothered by Dechtire. Take mother, son and their attending maidens back to Ulster. There the boy must be raised as a warrior.'

So Dechtire was taken back to Ulster where her husband Sualtam was overjoyed to be reunited with his bride and was happy to raise the boy as his own. They called him Setanta.

From the earliest age, Setanta showed remarkable skill at everything he did. There was no doubt that he was a son of Lug.

When Setanta was just seven years old, he ran away to the court of his uncle, King Conchobar. There, he was taught by Ulster's seven greatest heroes and poets – all deeply honoured to be his teacher.

By the time Setanta was twelve, he was stronger than most men, and loved to play hurley – a stick and ball game played between two teams. One day, Culan the blacksmith prepared a great feast at his hall for the king and his finest warriors, and Conchobar wanted Setanta to accompany him.

'But I'm in the middle of a game!' the boy called out, as the king's party came to a halt at the edge of the field. He gave the ball such a 'THWACK' with his stick that the opposing team scattered to avoid its path. 'I will join you there, uncle,' he said.

'Very well,' agreed the king, and he and his warriors went on to Culan's hall.

Soon the feast was underway, and Culan the blacksmith put his hound at the gates to stand guard while he entertained his king.

In all the merriment, Conchobar had completely forgotten that Setanta was yet to arrive and that he was not known to the dog...

So when the boy had finished the game of hurley – in which his team was, as always, victorious – he made his way to the great hall. The vicious, slavering guard dog attacked him at the gates. Fortunately for Setanta, he was not only very strong and very brave, but was also quick-thinking. He hurled the hurley ball at the beast's mouth and it became lodged in the dog's throat.

He then grabbed the startled creature by its hind legs and dashed its brains out against the wall.

'This child is truly the son of Lug,' gasped Culan, 'but there was no better guard dog than this hound. What protection can I offer now?'

Setanta heard the anger in his voice.

'I shall be your guard dog until a pup can be reared to take this one's place,' he announced.

And, from that moment on, Setanta became known as Cuchulain, which means the Hound of Culan.

When Cuchulain was first given weapons and a chariot, he went off at once to face the three sons of Nechtan. These three warriors had been terrorizing the innocent people of Ulster with their evil ways and powerful magic, and many a brave man had been slaughtered trying to rid the island of them.

But Cuchulain returned victorious, with the three heads of the slain brothers tied to the side of his chariot as trophies. He was a changed man – he had tasted blood, and would never be the same again. He challenged every warrior he met to mortal combat, and people came to fear him.

Finally, he was caught by a group of women who tossed him in a barrel of water to cool his fighting spirit... a spirit so strong that the hoops of the barrel melted. In a second barrel, he caused the water to bubble and boil, so they plunged him into a third. This final ducking was enough to bring Cuchulain to his senses.

After that, Cuchulain decided that it was time to take a wife. There was only one woman for him. And that was Emer, the daughter of Forgal the Wily. Wily means crafty and cunning, and Forgal was certainly that. When he discovered Cuchulain's interest in his daughter – and her interest in him – he sent the young hero on a quest.

Cuchulain was to visit Skye, one of the Western Isles of Scotland, where the island's queen, the warrior Scathac, would teach him how to become invincible. What Emer's wily father didn't tell the eager young Cuchulain was that Queen Scathac hated strangers and would surely kill him.

But Forgal had underestimated Cuchulain who was, after all, the son of Lug. He made his way across the Scottish highlands, fighting beasts, fording rivers and crossing a magic bridge that spanned a bottomless gorge, until he came upon Queen Scathac and took her by surprise.

She was impressed by his skills.

'It is rare to find one who can catch me unawares,' she said and, when he told her of the reason for his quest, the Scottish warrior queen agreed to teach Cuchulain all she knew.

With this knowledge, Cuchulain returned to Ireland to claim Emer as his wife. It was then that he discovered that her father, Forgal, was not true to his word. He had sent out his forces against him. But Cuchulain had little to worry about. He defeated them with ease and, when Forgal fled, he and Emer became husband and wife.

Perhaps Cuchulain's finest hour came in the battle called the Tain bo Cuailgne – the Cattle Raid of Cuailgne – when Queen Maeve of Connaught tried to seize a bull belonging to an Ulster chieftain.

This was a prize animal of great importance, so Maeve sent Fergus and his warriors to steal it. Once loyal to King Conchobar, Fergus had turned against him after the king's men had murdered his sons as they tried to protect doomed Deirdre from the prophecy.

Queen Maeve was sure that she would be victorious, because the warriors of Ulster were suffering from a terrible curse.

In times of trouble, their bodies became weakened for a while and they couldn't fight properly.

But Maeve hadn't reckoned on Cuchulain...

No curse could weaken him and he was ready to fight. His skeleton swivelled inside his skin, one eye grew huge and the other shrank, sparks poured from his mouth, his body hissed with heat and blood spurted from his head, filling the air with a thin, red haze.

Some could not even bear to look at him in this state and simply turned and fled. Those who faced him were killed in their hundreds every day of the battle.

So many men died that a deal had to be struck. Cuchulain agreed to face one champion each day. But, day after day, he defeated the enemy. Queen Maeve, meanwhile, managed to capture the bull but, by then, King Conchobar and his warriors had regained their strength, and Maeve and her forces were driven out of Ulster.

Cuchulain – the Hound of Culan – had many other adventures. He was finally slain up against a standing stone he'd lashed himself to so that he would die on his feet. There was no greater warrior than this.

THE CHANGELING OF GREEN KNOLL

Ireland is a place of magic and home to the Little People. If you catch one, he has to tell you where he's hidden his pot of gold. But Scotland has its Little People too, as this Celtic myth from the Western Isles reveals.

The Green Knoll stood on a small island, near a cluster of cottages huddled together as protection against the cold winds of the Atlantic Ocean. It was a round and smooth grassy hill, and did not look as if it had been made by the hand of God.

Some people said that it was a vast burrow – a burial chamber for an ancient people. Others said that it was home to the Little People – faeries who were rarely seen, but who got up to mischief in the village in the light of a full moon.

Many had tried to find an entrance into the Green Knoll, but without success. No one had dared to try digging their way in, because, whatever this strange hill was, there was a strong sense of magic about it. And no one in their right mind interferes with magic they do not understand.

Like the dwarfs of the Norse countries, these faeries were said to be skilled blacksmiths and fine weapon makers. They could beat beautiful swords, shields and spears out of the hot metal on their anvils. Some villagers swore they heard a muffled clanging coming from deep within the heart of the hill. Others said it was simply the sounds – blown across the hill by the wind – of their local blacksmith, Iain, at work in his smithy.

Iain was a hardworking man. He had hoped that his son would be his apprentice and work alongside him, one day taking over the smithy as his own. But the boy had always been lazy. Instead of helping his father he lay in bed, all day and every day, eating and drinking. That was all he ever seemed to do – eat and drink. But, however much he ate and drank, he always wanted more and stayed as thin as a fire poker.

Soon rumours began to spread around the village that the boy wasn't a human child at all, but a changeling. A changeling is a faery child, swapped with a real child soon after birth. He, or she, looks like a normal child but does not behave like one. There is something not quite right about a changeling, and now even Iain was beginning to suspect that this boy might not be his son at all.

'But how can I be sure?' he said, one night, seated with his friends around a table in a farmer's croft. 'For, if this is not my son, the Little People must have him and I must find a way of rescuing him.'

'I've heard that these changelings lead many lives,' said the farmer. 'They may look like children, but they are hundreds of years old.'

'I've heard that too,' said the farmer's wife. 'And I've also heard that they like nothing more than to see something truly extraordinary – something they haven't seen in all their years.'

'But how does that help me?' asked Iain the blacksmith.

'Because it is said that, on seeing such an extraordinary sight, a changeling cannot help but give himself away by crying out in amazement in his true voice,' explained the woman.

'But what fantastic things can we show him here on our small island?' sighed Iain.

Just then the door to the croft blew open and, framed against the night sky stood an old man.

'Simple things can be made to seem extraordinary,' he said. 'The next time your son demands a drink, here is what you must do...'

And the blacksmith and his friends listened with wide-eyed amazement.

Later that day, the boy demanded a drink.

A moment later, following the old man's instructions, the blacksmith came into the boy's bedroom with half an eggshell filled with water in each hand.

Although eggshells are as light as light can be, and they hold very little water, the blacksmith pretended that they were as heavy as his anvil and that he had to drag himself across the room for the weight of them. He placed them at the boy's bedside with a groan, and wiped his brow, looking exhausted.

The boy laughed. 'In all the hundreds of years I've lived, I've never seen such an extraordinary sight as that!' he squealed in delight and, unaware that he had been tricked into giving himself away as a changeling, promptly demanded supper.

Now it was time for Iain the blacksmith to put the next part of the old man's plan into action, to rid himself of this changeling.

He began to build a large fire by the boy's bed.

'What are you doing, father?' he asked.

'You'll soon see,' said the blacksmith and, when the fire was roaring hot, he snatched the boy and threw him towards the flames.

Before he had time to reach the fire, the changeling flew up in the air and smashed his way through the roof and out of the house forever.

Iain hurried to find the old man who was staying in the local tavern.

'I've proved that the thing I brought up as my son is of faery birth,' he said. 'But how will I ever get my true son back? How can I ever hope to find him?'

'He is inside the Green Knoll,' said the man who, as well as being very old, was very wise. 'But the only way in or out is on the night of a full moon when a great door appears in its side... a door which disappears at dawn.'

'But it's a full moon tonight!' cried Iain.

'Which is why you must act quickly,' said the old man.

Once again, he told the blacksmith exactly what to do.

Shivering with fear as well as cold, Iain the blacksmith made his way around the Green Knoll, bathed in silvery moonlight. And there, sure enough, was a huge door.

He reached out his hand and placed it on this magical entrance which seemed to be made out of moonlight itself and was as cold as silver to the touch. It swung open. Clutching a Bible in one hand, and keeping a firm hold on a rooster hidden under his coat in the other – just as the old man had instructed – he took one last gulp of night air, then stepped into the blackness.

Now the frightened blacksmith was inside the hill, walking down a tunnel towards a warm, orange glow that came from the very heart of the Green Knoll.

As he drew nearer, he could hear the familiar 'CLANK', 'CLANK' of skilled hands at work with a hammer and anvil, beating hot metal into shape. He found himself in a great hallway. There, scurrying around on the stone floor, and each of them no higher than his knee, were hoards of Little People. They paid no attention to him, for they were busy working the bellows of a fire, and fetching metal and tools to an anvil at which a human boy – towering above them – was hard at work.

Iain gasped out loud, for here was his true son.

The Little People heard the blacksmith's gasp and turned, as one, to face him.

'Be gone and we will not harm you,' their leader squealed. 'If you stay, and dawn comes, you too will be prisoner when the doorway melts away with the moonlight!'

'I'm not afraid of you,' said Iain, bravely, holding the Bible out in front of him for protection.

What the Little People didn't know was that Iain had also let the rooster out from under his coat. On seeing the warm glow of the fire where the irons were being heated, the bird thought this was the first sign of dawn and began to crow a rooster's greeting to the sun.

The Little People were thrown into a panic – just as the old man had intended as part of his plan for Iain to rescue his son.

They thought that it really was dawn, which meant that the doorway would close, shutting some of the Little People – who were off mischief-making – out of the Green Knoll until the next full moon. In the commotion, Iain grabbed his son with one hand and, still clutching the Bible in the other, dashed for the exit.

By the time the Little People realized they'd been tricked by a confused rooster, the blacksmith was safely back in his smithy. And his son was safely back in the world of humans where he belonged.

INDEX

Ainle, a Son of Usnech 5, 21, 22
Ardan, a Son of Usnech 5, 21, 22
Arianrod, mother of Llew 4, 5, 6–10
Arthur, King of the Britons 2, 3, 4, 5,
  25–9, 30–5
Avalon, the island where King Arthur
  lies sleeping 35

Balor, a Fomorian chieftain with an
  evil eye 4, 16–17
bards, wandering poets 9
Bedivere, Sir, one of Arthur's knights 34,35
Blodeuwedd, wife of Llew 4, 11

Camelot, King Arthur's castle 29, 31, 32
Cathbad, the Druid 19, 21, 22, 23
Celtic heroes 4–5
Celtic peoples 2, 3
changelings, faery children 4, 44, 45
Conchobar, King of Ulster 4, 5, 19–23,
  37–41
Cuchulain, Ireland's greatest warrior 4, 5,
  37–41
Culan, a blacksmith 4, 5, 38, 39, 41

Dechtire, mother of Cuchulain 4, 37, 38
Deirdre, daughter of Fedlimid 4, 5, 18–23,
  40
Diancecht, father of Miach 16

Ector, Sir, King Arthur's guardian 25–9
Emer, wife of Cuchulain 4, 40
Excalibur, King Arthur's sword 31, 34, 35

faeries 4, 5, 43, 44, 45
Fedlimid, father of Deirdre 4, 19, 20
Fergus, an Irish hero 21, 22, 40
fidchell, a board game 14
Fomors, hideous giants 4, 5, 13, 15–17
Forgal, the Wily 4, 40

Gaelic language 2
Gaheris, Sir, one of Arthur's knights 33
Gareth, Sir, one of Arthur's knights 33
Gaul, an ancient country 2
Green Knoll, home of the Little People
  42, 43, 45, 46, 47
Guinevere, King Arthur's queen 4, 5, 30,
  31, 32, 33

Gwydion, father of Llew 4, 5, 6–11
Gwynedd, a Welsh realm 5, 10

Holy Grail 31
hurley, a stick and ball game 38, 39

jousting 25–8

Kay, Sir, son of Sir Ector 26–9
Knights of the Round Table 29, 31, 32,
  33 see also under individual names, eg
  Lancelot

Lady of the Lake 31, 35
Lancelot, Sir, Arthur's greatest knight
  5, 30, 31, 32, 33
Levarcham, Deirdre's foster mother
  20, 21, 22
Little People 4, 5, 43, 46, 47
Llew Llaw Gyffes, a Welsh hero 4, 5, 6–11
Lucan, Sir, one of Arthur's knights 34
Lug, High King of Ireland 4, 5, 12–17,
  37, 38, 39, 40

Macha, warrior queen of King Nuada 16
Maeve, Queen of Connaught 40, 41
Math, a ruler and sorcerer 4, 5, 10, 11
Merlin, the magician 29, 30, 31
Miach, a healer 14, 16
Mordred, traitor to King Arthur 32, 33, 34

Naoise, a Son of Usnech 5, 20–3
Nuada, King of the Tuatha Dé Danann
  5, 13–16

Ogma, champion of Tara 14, 15

prophecies 19, 20, 21, 23, 32

Red Branch, King Conchobar's great
  warriors 19, 20, 21, 22, 23
Romans 2
Romanticism, an artistic movement 3

Scathac, a Scottish warrior queen 40
Setanta, later known as Cuchulain 5, 36,
  38, 39
Sualtam, a chieftain 37, 38
Sword in the Stone 24–9, 31

Tara, high seat of the Irish Kings 13, 14, 15
trickery 7–11
Tuatha Dé Danann, rulers of all Ireland
  5, 14, 15, 16, 17

Uther Pendragon, King of the Britons
  before Arthur 25, 29, 31

yew trees 23

First published in the UK in 1998 by

Belitha Press Ltd
  London House, Great Eastern Wharf,
  Parkgate Road, London SW11 4NQ

ISBN 1 85561 804 4

British Library Cataloguing in Publication
Data for this book is available from the
British Library.

Editor: Julie Hill
Designer: Jamie Asher
Educational consultant: Liz Bassant
Series editor: Mary-Jane Wilkins

Printed in Hong Kong